GRADE **PK**

The Smart Alec Series™

MATH READINESS

SUPER MAN

MACHO

MAN

BOY

Wheel of Fortune

3 BALLS $1

POWER PITCH

#1

POWER PITCH

HIT - 1 PRIZE
HITS - 2 PRIZES
HIT - TRADE
SMALL PRIZES
1 BIG PRIZE

ep edgeucational publishing

MAKE IT FUN!

Dear Parent/Caregiver,

Introduce your child to important early number concepts including number recognition, counting, one-to-one correspondence, more than, less than, and same as.

There are many fun and simple math activities you can do with your child:

- When it's snack time, have your child count out a specific number of cookies, pretzels or pieces of fruit.

- Ask your child to assist when you set the table. Let him, or her, count how many people will be at the table and determine how many plates, forks, napkins, etc. you need to set the table.

- Make a game of clean up time. Give instructions such as, "Pick up six toys." Ask questions such as, "How many have you picked up so far?"

- Encourage your child to help you any time you need a specific number of a particular item. Give instructions such as, "May I please have two apples?"

The more fun you make each activity, the more your child will benefit. This book provides you with a stepping stone in your child's education. You are an integral part of your child's ability to succeed. Get started today and have fun!

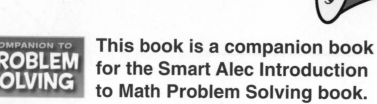

COMPANION TO PROBLEM SOLVING

This book is a companion book for the Smart Alec Introduction to Math Problem Solving book.

Table of Contents

Hi! I'm Smart Alec!

Zippy Zero

Zero 0

Hi!
I'm Smart Alec

Trace the numbers.

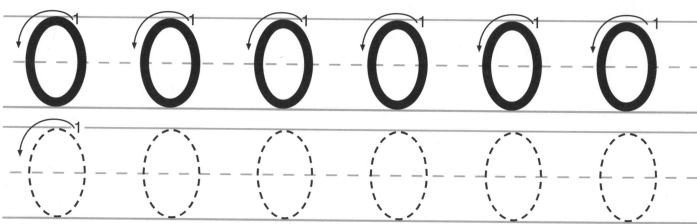

Practice writing the number 0.

Fun With One

One 1

Trace the numbers.

Practice writing the number 1.

Terrific Two

Two 2

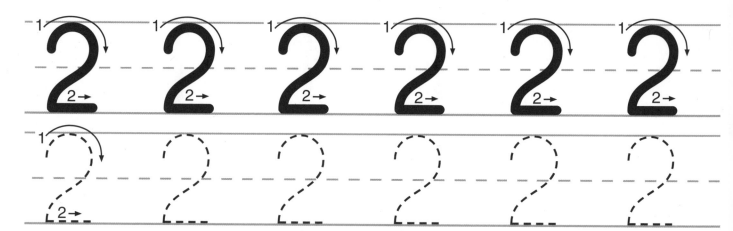

Trace the numbers.

Practice writing the number 2.

Three Cheers for Three

Three 3

Trace the numbers.

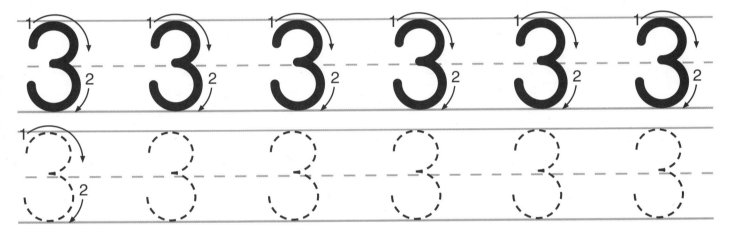

Practice writing the number 3.

Fabulous Four

Four 4

Trace the numbers.

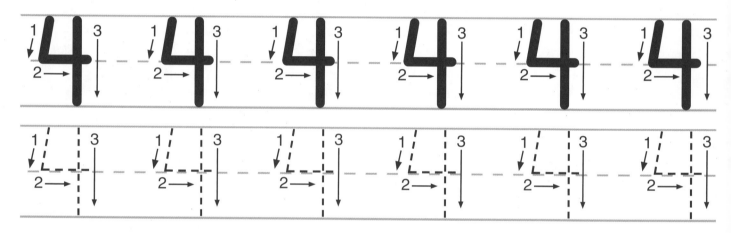

Practice writing the number 4.

Fantastic Five

Five 5

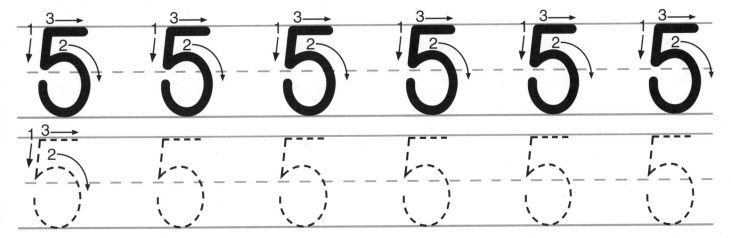

Trace the numbers.

Practice writing the number 5.

Spectacular Six

Six 6

Trace the numbers.

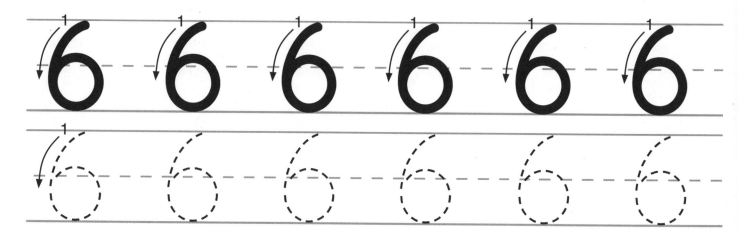

Practice writing the number 6.

Seven 7

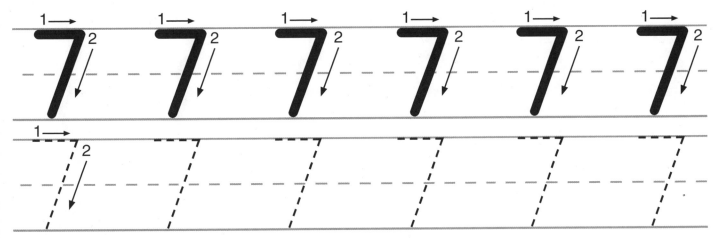

Trace the numbers.

Practice writing the number 7.

Eight 8

Trace the numbers.

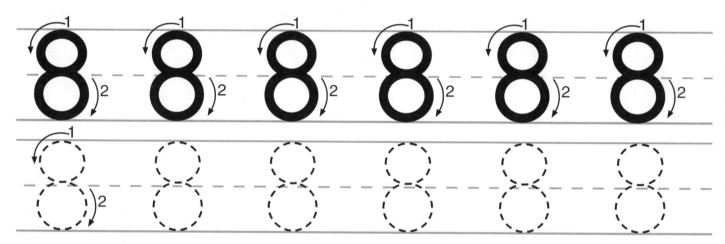

Practice writing the number 8.

Nifty Nine

Nine 9

Trace the numbers.

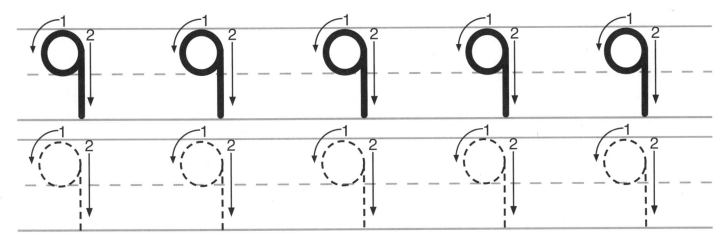

Practice writing the number 9.

Ten 10

Trace the numbers.

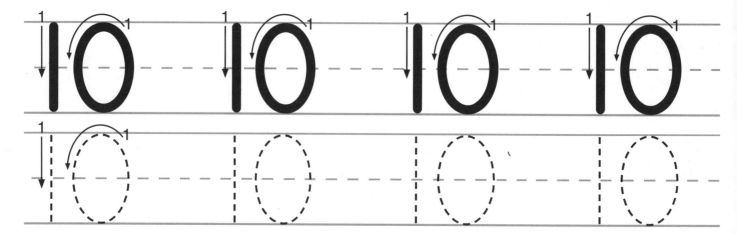

Practice writing the number 10.

Number Match

How many dragonflies are in each box?
Circle the number in that box.

Bug Match

Draw a line from the number to the matching group.

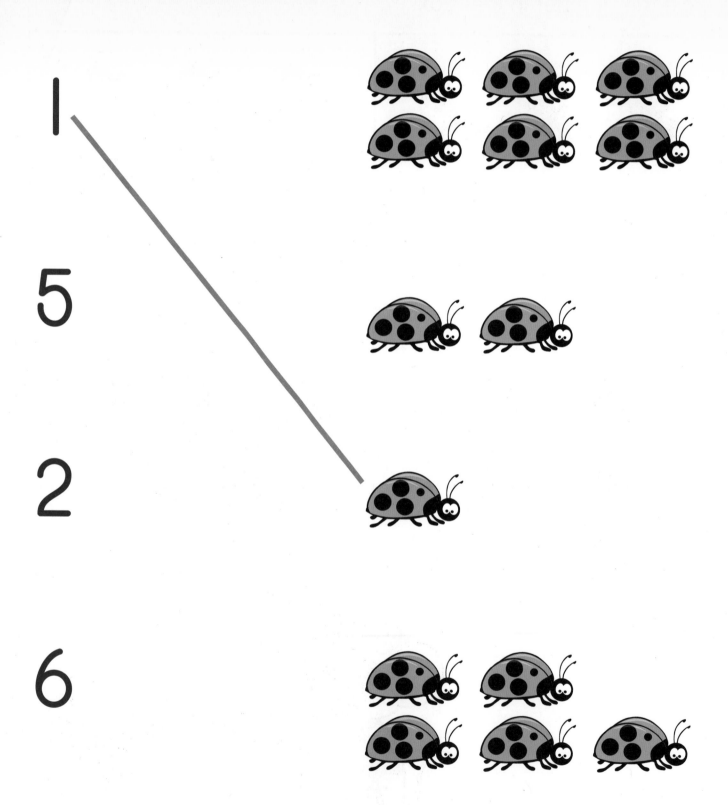

Bug Count

Count. Write the correct number.

5

Bug Search

Count and write how many.

How many flowers?  6

How many bees?  - - -

How many ladybugs?  - - -

Count and Color

Color 4 ants

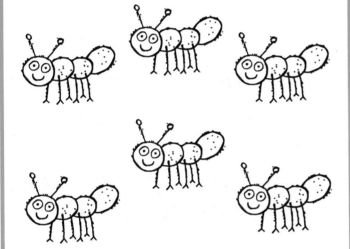

Color 2 ladybugs

Color 3 beehives

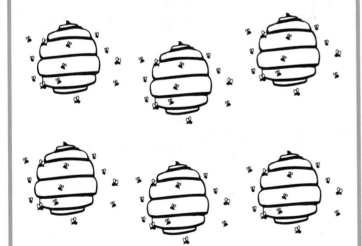

Color 5 butterflies

Counting Fun

Cross out the correct number of ladybugs in each row.

7

5

3

9

2

6

Count with Dominoes

Count the total number of dots on each domino.
Write the number.

4

Connect-the-Dots

Connect the dots from zero to ten.

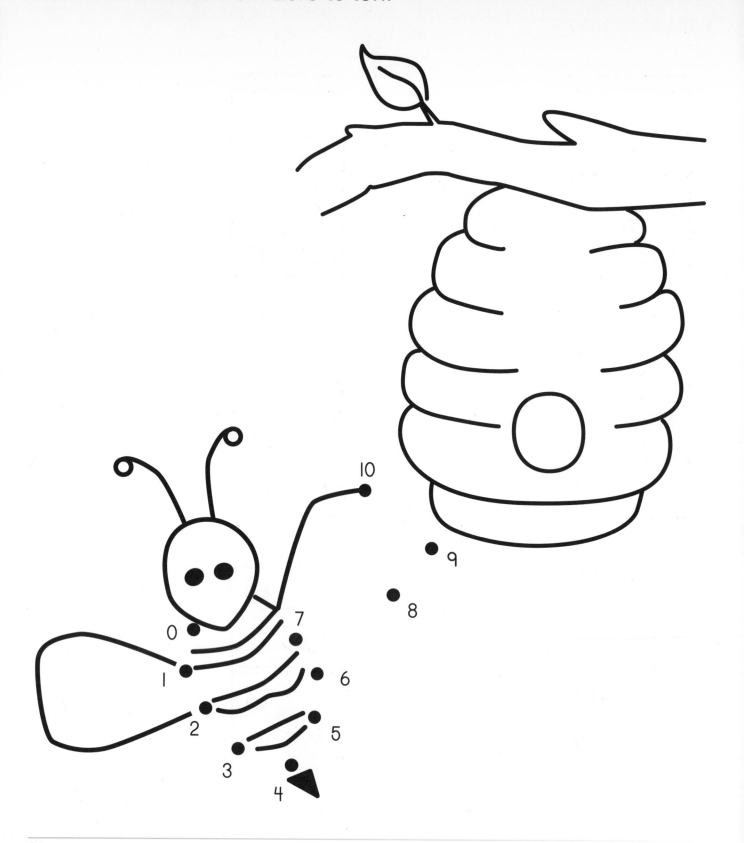

Zero, One, and Two

Trace the number words.

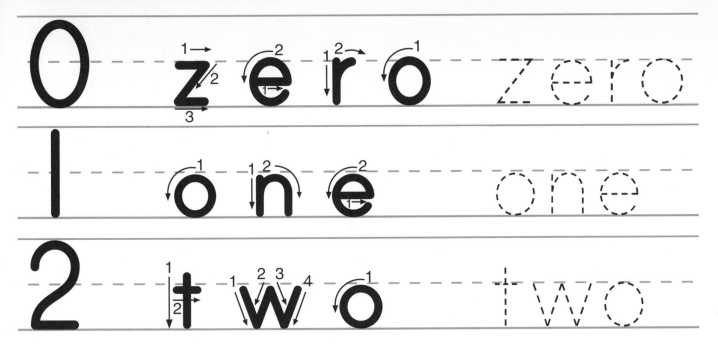

Match the number to the word.

0

2

1

one

zero

two

Three and Four

Trace the number words.

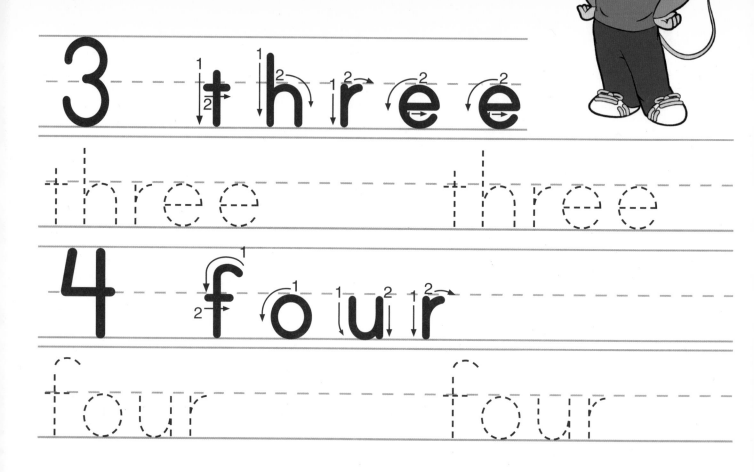

Circle the matching numbers.

four   4   2   1   4

three   6   3   7   3

Five and Six

Trace the number words.

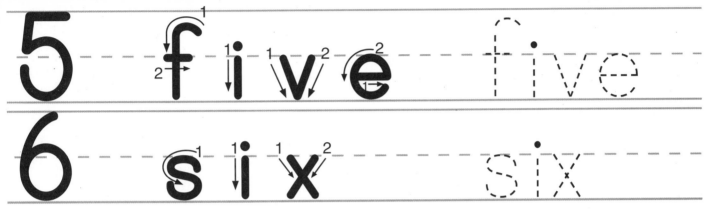

Match the number to the word.

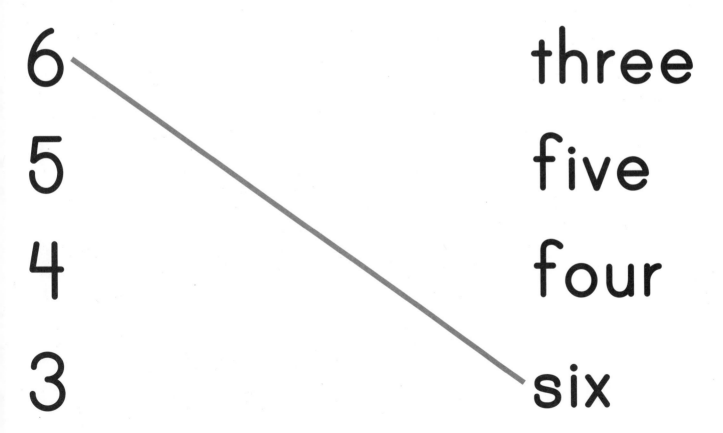

6
5
4
3

three
five
four
six

Seven and Eight

Trace the number words.

7 seven seven

8 eight eight

Match the number to the picture.

8
3
2
7

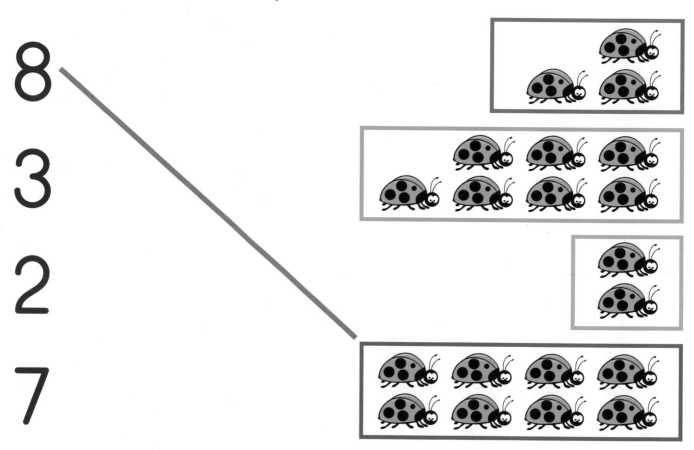

Nine and Ten

Trace the number words.

9 nine   nine

10 ten   ten

Circle all of the 9s and 10s.

8   6   3   9

    10   7   5

9   1   4   10

More, More, More

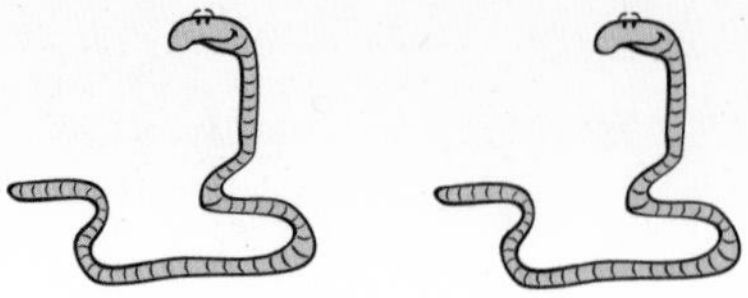

Two worms

More worms

Draw one more worm.

How many in all?

_____
_ _ _
_____

Draw two more worms.

How many in all?

_____
_ _ _
_____

Less, Less, Less

Three ants

Less ants

Color less than 3 ants.

Color less than 5 ants.

More or Less?

Circle the ladybug with **more** than five (5) spots.

Circle the ladybugs with **less** than five (5) spots.

Is It the Same Number?

Three bugs   **Three bugs**

Same

Draw the same number of dots on the other domino.

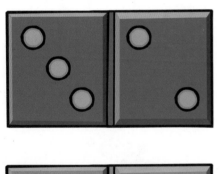   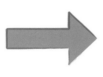   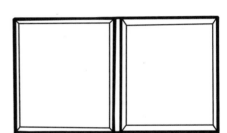

   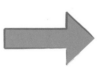   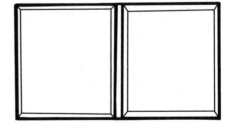

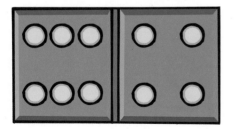   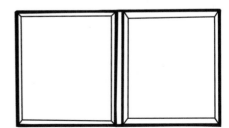

Count and Circle

Count each group. Circle the matching number.

Missing Numbers

Fill in the missing numbers.

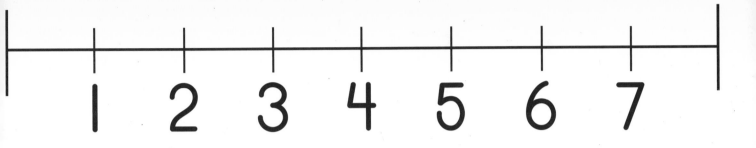

1 2 3 4 5 6 7

0, 1, 2, 3

4, ___, 6, ___

2, 3, ___, 5

1, ___, 3, 4, ___

Number Search

Circle all of the 7s.

9 (7) 5 (7) 3 2

Circle all of the 2s.

1 2 8 2 4 6

Circle all of the 0s.

0 9 3 0 6 0

Domino Dots

Count the dots on each domino.
Circle the correct number.

3   (6)   9

5   9   4

10   6   4

2   3   5

Picture Time!

Draw four (4) wings on the butterfly.

Draw six (6) spots on each wing.

Draw two (2) antennae.

Draw six (6) legs on the body.

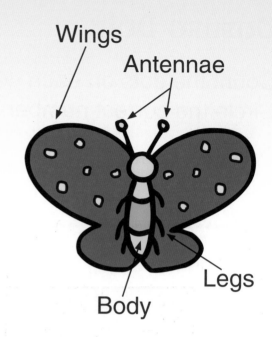

Wings

Antennae

Legs

Body

Number Match

Match each number to the correct group.
Draw a line from the picture to the correct number.

3

10

5

7

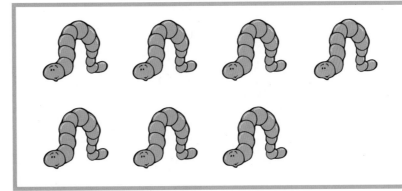

Writing Numbers Review

Trace and write each number.

Finger Count

Count the fingers. Circle the number that shows
the correct number of fingers.

2 (6) 4   9 7 5

1 3 10   6 8 2

Answer Key

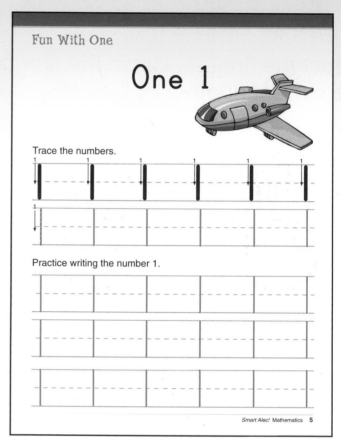

Fabulous Four

Four 4

Trace the numbers.

Practice writing the number 4.

Fantastic Five

Five 5

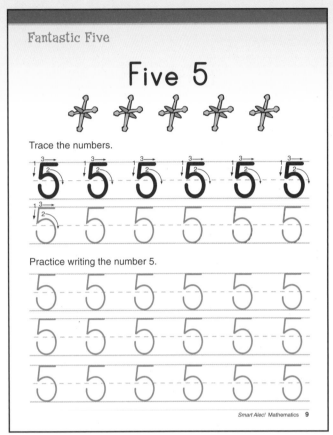

Trace the numbers.

Practice writing the number 5.

Spectacular Six

Six 6

Trace the numbers.

Practice writing the number 6.

Super Seven

Seven 7

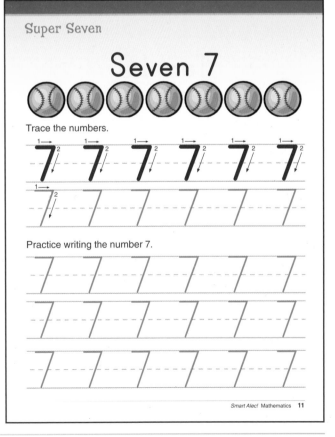

Trace the numbers.

Practice writing the number 7.

Eight 8

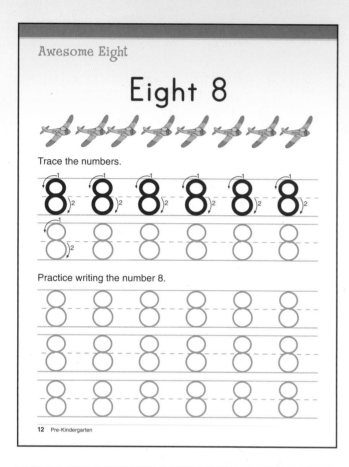

Trace the numbers.

Practice writing the number 8.

Nine 9

Trace the numbers.

Practice writing the number 9.

Ten 10

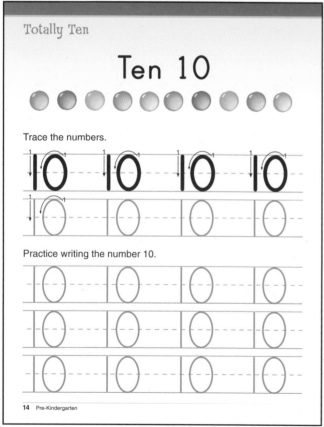

Trace the numbers.

Practice writing the number 10.

How many dragonflies are in each box?
Circle the number in that box.

4 ③ 6   5 7 ⑥

2 9 ④   8 1 ⑤

Bug Match

Draw a line from the number to the matching group.

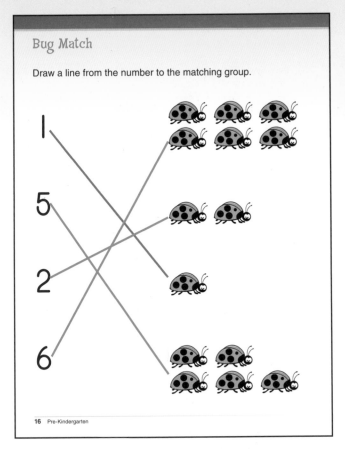

Bug Count

Count. Write the correct number.

Bug Search

Count and write how many.

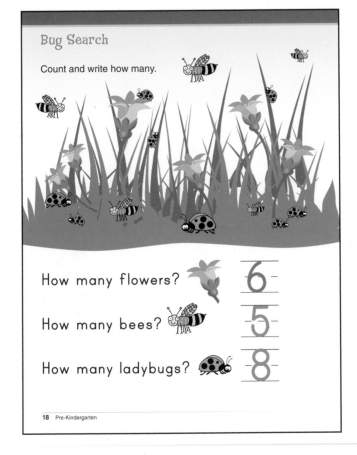

How many flowers?   6

How many bees?   5

How many ladybugs?   8

Count and Color

Color 4 ants

Color 2 ladybugs

Color 3 beehives

Color 5 butterflies

Counting Fun

Cross out the correct number of ladybugs in each row.

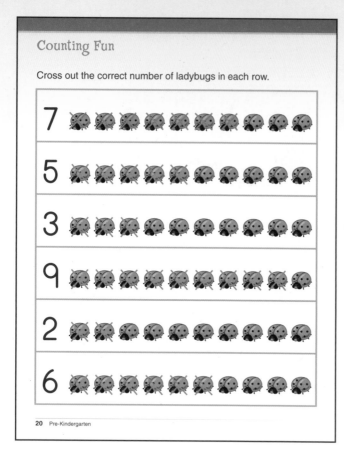

Count with Dominoes

Count the total number of dots on each domino.
Write the number.

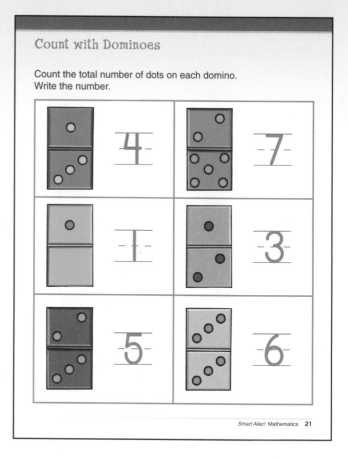

Connect-the-Dots

Connect the dots from zero to ten.

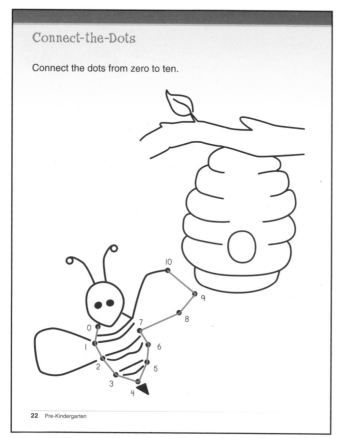

Zero, One, and Two

Trace the number words.

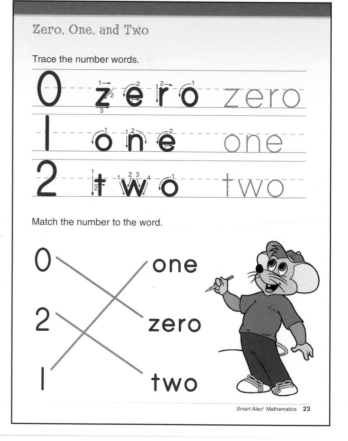

Match the number to the word.

Three and Four

Trace the number words.

Circle the matching numbers.

four   (4)   2   1   (4)

three   6   (3)   7   (3)

Five and Six

Trace the number words.

Match the number to the word.

6   three

5   five

4   four

3   six

Seven and Eight

Trace the number words.

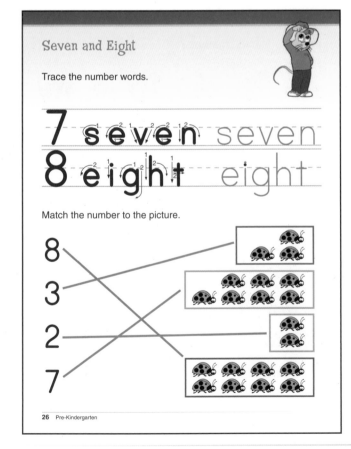

Match the number to the picture.

8

3

2

7

Nine and Ten

Trace the number words.

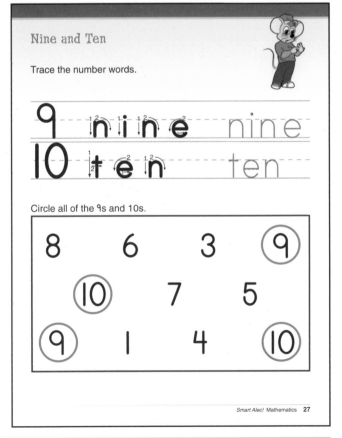

Circle all of the 9s and 10s.

8   6   3   (9)

(10)   7   5

(9)   1   4   (10)

More, More, More

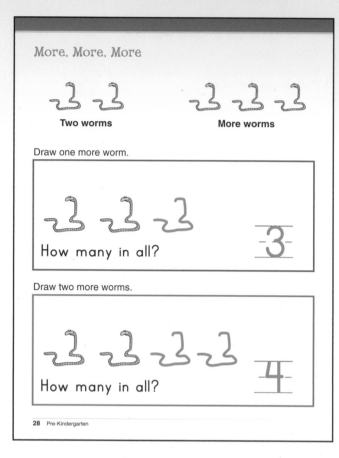

Two worms

More worms

Draw one more worm.

How many in all? 3

Draw two more worms.

How many in all? 4

Less, Less, Less

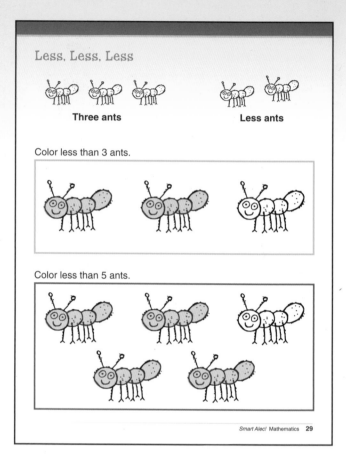

Three ants

Less ants

Color less than 3 ants.

Color less than 5 ants.

More or Less?

Circle the ladybug with **more** than five (5) spots.

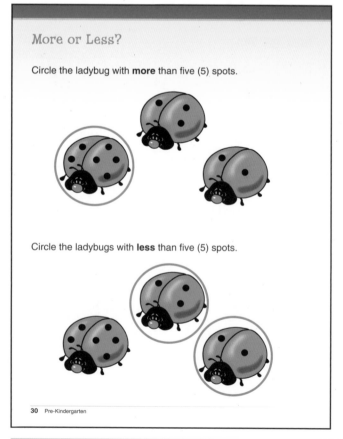

Circle the ladybugs with **less** than five (5) spots.

Is It the Same Number?

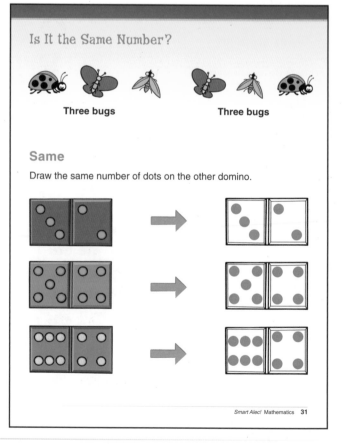

Three bugs

Three bugs

Same

Draw the same number of dots on the other domino.

Count and Circle

Count each group. Circle the matching number.

Missing Numbers

Fill in the missing numbers.

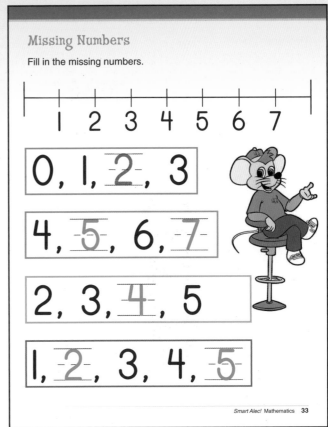

Number Search

Circle all of the 7s.

Circle all of the 2s.

Circle all of the 0s.

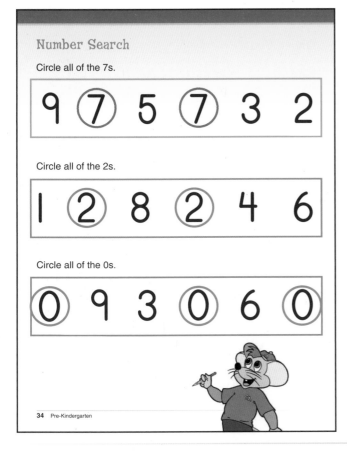

Domino Dots

Count the dots on each domino.
Circle the correct number.

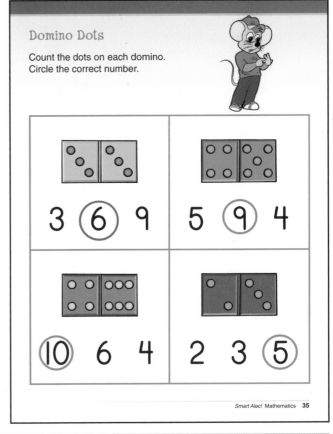

Picture Time!

Draw four (4) wings on the butterfly.

Draw six (6) spots on each wing.

Draw two (2) antennae.

Draw six (6) legs on the body.

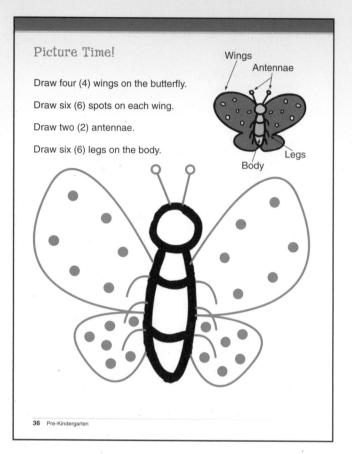

Number Match

Match each number to the correct group.
Draw a line from the picture to the correct number.

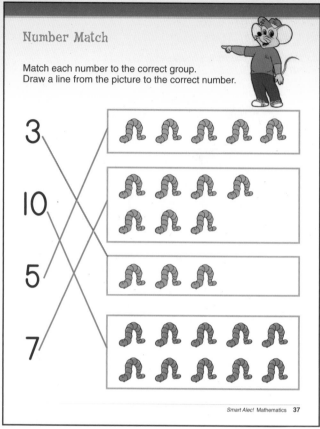

Writing Numbers Review

Trace and write each number.

Finger Count

Count the fingers. Circle the number that shows the correct number of fingers.

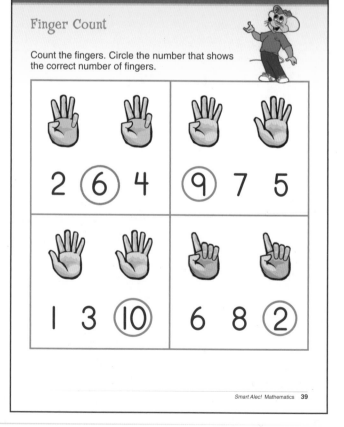